Disrupting Fitness

Four Paradigms Shifts
to Live an Infinity Lifestyle

Mr1nf1n1ty

Table of Contents

Foreword

What you are holding in your hand is energy. You were led to this book just as much as I was led to write this book. It is not an accident that you heard about this book and decided to purchase it. You brought this book into your reality, which means there is something in here that is aligned with where you currently are and where you want to go. Now, be forewarned -- the information found in this book will challenge you. How do I know? Because it challenges me every single day. It is counterintuitive to what we have been taught and programmed to believe.

However, if you are like me, you know that there is a significant paradigm shift that is happening on this Earth, and you are either catching it and making changes, or you are firmly planting your feet in the ground, resolving to stay the same. But the fact that you are holding this book in your hands tells me that you are ready to make the shift as well.

This isn't just words on a page. These concepts have the power to change your life as they have done to mine and are continuing to do. As we navigate these paradigm shifts, know that I'm shifting with you. Know that I haven't got this all figured out. I'm still on this journey just like you are. So, we are moving through this together as we learn from one another. Keep your mind and spirit open throughout this process, and you will find the answers you've been looking for within yourself. Let's do this.

Chapter 1

The Disruption

The lowest points, the rock bottoms, and the moments when life seems to crumble around you can be the most defining, if you allow them to be. It is only then that you can start to become someone new. That is the real evolution. When you choose to make growth a non-negotiable, you don't run from the low points. You don't avoid the rock bottoms. You don't numb your hard moments with addictions or feed them with every distraction that surrounds you. Instead, you learn to lean in, endure the pain and listen to the voice within that's giving you the direction you need, even if it only comes in small nudges.

One particularly defining low point for me occurred during a time when I was experiencing a great deal of success with the promise of even more to come. In fact, I had already achieved considerable success and accolades that people spend their lives striving for. From a young age, I always had an entrepreneurial mindset. I was a hustler and had a crazy work ethic with everything I pursued. The way I approached life and my perspective on reality marked me as uncommon among my peers and even family members. People around me never really understood me and spent more time mocking me. I was somewhat of an outcast, but at the same time I was popular and athletic, which garnered me a lot of attention from my peers. To put it simply, I was cool but weird as fuck.

Sports were at the center of my life during high school, which allowed me to play college ball at a high level. After college graduation, I went to play ball overseas in Norway. This ended up being one of the greatest experiences of my life since I was more focused than I had ever been. But at the same time, I was incredibly homesick. Uprooting my life to go to a place that presented a completely different way of life and culture was difficult at first. But instead of merely surrendering to the discomfort, I became fueled by it. I started writing the phrase "OneLife" on all the rubber bands I wore around my wrist. It served as a reminder for me to stay present and in the moment. When I saw that phrase, it became a command to my subconscious mind to shift my focus towards gratitude and savoring the current moment because I knew it wouldn't always be this way. I could capitalize on the opportunity I had been given, or I could squander it by wishing I was somewhere else with someone else doing something else.

OneLife started out as just a phrase that helped me focus, but then slowly it became a vision for something greater. Once I got back to Indianapolis, Indiana, which was my hometown, I hit the ground running. I trademarked the name OneLife as a sportswear company and ironically enough, the guy who had previously held the trademark had relinquished it after twenty years. So, I took that as a sign that it was divine. That name became the jumping off point for the innovation and creativity that was starting to define my life.

My intention had never been to find a traditional job. I had never taken jobs too seriously nor was I scared to quit a job, even if it meant I had to live on the streets. I was never scared to go to the bottom and believed that if I wasn't happy, then that meant I wasn't supposed to be there, doing what I was doing. This mindset didn't really mesh well with those around me in Indianapolis who seemed to be driven by a slavish or dependent mindset. Most people were looking for bullshit jobs that were unfulfilling and kept them in a state of lack.

OneLife grew quickly as I continued to innovate and get creative with what I could do with my skills. I opened a yoga and Pilates studio, trained pro athletes, and sold OneLife gear. As my business gained notoriety in Indianapolis, I was also receiving calls from NBA coaches asking me to come try out. At the time, I was considered one of the best basketball players in Indiana, so even my friends were encouraging me to pursue a career in the NBA. To this day, I'm not sure why I didn't go down this avenue since the end goal of my basketball career had always been to play for the NBA. And yet, I never went to any tryouts. I also had the option to go back overseas to play ball, but it just didn't seem like the right move for me.

Despite the success I was experiencing, my life didn't align with what society or other people thought I should have. I spent most of my time in the gym and didn't get into the chase of trying to get girls, possessions, or more money. Financially, I was comfortable, but at the same time, I was working way too hard. On top of that, I had a heavy burden of responsibility on my shoulders. I had people looking at me with their hands out for a piece of what I was building, and I wasn't prepared to handle all those hands. A lot of people thought I was doing better than I was, so they didn't seek to add to my life; rather, they wanted to subtract. They may not have been consciously doing it, but most people I had been around were programmed to take energy instead of bring value. This is still true as I have found most people want to see what they can get as opposed to what they can contribute. I call these people energy vampires and at that time, I was surrounded by them.

My well was running dry, and I didn't realize it. I was tired all the time, but my hunger and work ethic wouldn't let me rest. The problem wasn't with my work, the problem was that I was ignorant on how to find the balance I needed, which could only come through the practice of key spiritual laws that now guide my life. It was then that a major paradigm shift started to occur. The message I was receiving from the Universe was that a change needed to happen. I was stuck in a cesspool of fear, greed, and ignorance that was trapping me. I needed to break free.

The Universe has never really allowed me to become comfortable or to settle for a condition in life that is not serving me or others. But don't get me wrong, despite my outer circumstance and inner unrest, life had been pretty good. However, I was becoming overwhelmed by life, and since I was always different than those around me, I went within to get the answers. I've found that you've got to be willing to be different and go through some hard shit to become greater than who you are now. You can't be afraid of the pain or the cost you have to pay. And I was fully embracing the uncertainty I was feeling. Because with the uncertainty came deeper revelations that I had always had about the world around me. These concepts are more widely accepted now, but 20 years ago, people thought I was a lunatic.

Some of my revelations were that the FDA was fucking people through the food we were eating; our thoughts were being controlled; the television was programming us; there are only seven families that run the media with strategic propaganda; and the Big Pharma industry knows they are killing people for their bottom line. When I shared this stuff, people thought I was crazy, but I didn't care. I was having lucid dreams and studying more woke shit than I ever had before.

Every night I would read a portion of a book, and in one particular book I was reading by Grant Cardone, he kept writing about a place called LaJolla, CA. For some reason, this place kept being repeated to me while I read that book and long after I closed it. Then, I heard it. First it was a nudge, then it became a command that required action. My Spirit said, it's time to leave. And without telling a single soul, I started making plans to leave Indiana and travel all the way to California.

I didn't even know if my 1997 black Acura was going to make it all the way to California, but I was so resolute I didn't care about any consequence. If I died, then I died. I didn't know how the fuck I was going to get out of Indiana, but I was ready to go. So, for the next 2-3 weeks after I received the message, I started clearing stuff out of my life. I was aware of how energy works, so I knew that to accept something new, I would have to clear out what no longer served me. I was giving shit away and selling off stuff - really nice stuff. I was cleaning and organizing everything to get situated. I tried to get as much cash as I could so I could leave as quickly as possible.

On the morning I left, I hadn't told a single soul of my plans. I didn't want to hear the pushback or explain the decision I knew deep within that I had to make. Plus, I didn't have a detailed plan for how I was going to make this work, which I knew would disappoint those who would have questions. So, with $500 in my bank account and a light only shining on the next step directly in front of me, I left Indiana.

As I drove, all I did was listen to audiobooks that were feeding my mind and spirit. One book I was listening to was, "Ask and it is Given" by Abraham Hicks. It was like the words I was hearing were preparing me for the journey ahead. The drive seemed like it took forever. I was sleeping in my car and made stops along the way. My first stop was in St. Louis, MO to see an old college buddy who became a party promoter. The day I came to visit, he had a party that he wanted me to come to. I've never been a party dude, so when I got to the club, I stayed in the back while watching everyone look awkward. I could only take so much before I went outside to get some air.

About 6 feet from the entrance of the club, a homeless man approached me and asked for money. Little did he know I was on the street, too. Even though he told me he was a crackhead, there was something intriguing about this man. I looked at him and asked him how old he was. He said he was 42, but he looked 21. I said, "What the fuck? You are 42! Man, get the fuck out of here. How do you look so young?"

He responded by saying, "I figured out that I don't have to eat as much as they tell me I have to eat." He said all he did was eat a little bit of rice every day, and then he spent the rest of his money on dope.

We started talking and probably sat outside for 2 hours. I was locked into everything he was sharing. It was like he was meant to be teaching me about spiritual laws. It was as if he was building upon a foundation that I had already constructed but just didn't know how to add to that knowledge. He put me on so much game that night, and I'll be indebted to him for the rest of my life.

My friends couldn't believe I spent so much time talking to a crackhead, but little did they know the wisdom he shared with me was just what I had needed to continue on my journey. That situation taught me to never judge someone based on how they present. There are spiritual teachers everywhere if you are willing to remain open to what the Universe brings into your life.

My next stops were Nashville, TN and then New Mexico to visit friends. I didn't have any money, so I was just figuring it out along the way. It was $20 here and another $20 there, which at the time felt like so much money since I had very little. But the Universe was making it work for me. In the Bible, it says, "Ask and it is given," and I discovered the true meaning of this on my journey. If you are focused and going somewhere, the Universe will move heaven and earth to make it a reality. But, if you can never hold a focus and are easily distracted, then it won't happen. Once you hold a focus, you will get there because it's just in your mind - and whatever is in your mind, you will create it in your physical reality. We'll explore this more later on in the book.

When people asked why I was going to California, I would lie and tell them I had a job in San Diego. Once I arrived in California, I immediately found the nearest LA Fitness and applied for a job. They hired me on the spot, which meant I had a place to work, a place to shower, a place to work out, a place to park so I could sleep at night, and a place to shop since Walmart was right across the street. I would rough it every night. It's funny because there were four or five other cars that were in the LA Fitness parking lot each night as well. Just like me, there would be people in the front seats of their cars with their feet kicked up on the dashboard, and we would all go into the gym in the morning to take a shower. This actually brought me comfort because many times, especially through hard times, we feel like we are by ourselves. But you aren't by yourself, even when you think you are.

The irony was, even though by all accounts it seemed to be a difficult time for me, I wasn't tripping because I was having fun. I was playing basketball every day and met really great people. I was doing this for about a year. Looking back at that time in my life, I can see that this was such a pivotal moment for my spiritual awakening process. At the time, I didn't really know what it was that I was experiencing, but I was having a lot of synchronistic experiences. I also had my number codes around me all the time and a weird awareness about what was going on within and around me. I was aware that I wasn't my body. I was aware that I could shift my reality by shifting my perspective. I was aware of how powerful gratitude and visualization were. I was aware of the spiritual tools, but I didn't really have a name or a category for them. What I have discovered is that I was being thrust into a process headfirst that was moving me from what is called the third dimension paradigm into the fifth dimension paradigm.

Third v. Fifth dimension

Before we jump into the discussion on the characteristics of the third dimension and fifth dimension, I want to talk directly to you for a moment. You picked up this book for a reason, whether that be out of sheer curiosity, or like me, you are going through somewhat of an awakening and are looking for tools to help you navigate your journey. Either way, the concepts in this book are going to challenge you - mentally, physically, emotionally, and spiritually. Some of you may not be ready for this level of information. Your mind may not be able to fully grasp it yet, and that is okay. I'm not for everyone, just like my message isn't for everyone. But for the rest of you, the tools and concepts I share with you in this book will be exactly what you need to continue to create your own reality instead of being fed a false reality that is keeping you trapped.

I truly believe that the Earth is shifting from the third dimension into the fifth dimension, but some people are experiencing so much upheaval in their lives because they are still trying to fit back into the third dimension. Until they evolve out of that, they will be going through hell because the Earth as we knew it isn't there anymore. There was a point when we were in a physical, more matter-based and systematic Earth. But now that the Earth has literally shifted into a whole other place, if you aren't living unattached; if you aren't living in love; and if you aren't living in a fifth dimensional paradigm, you are going to be fucked up.

Here is the harsh reality - we have been sold a lie. We have been programmed to believe that what is tangible is real and what is intangible is merely a creation of the mind. However, that belief is what keeps so many people trapped. When you are more in an ego form and feel like you are your body and these physical things define you, you are living in a third dimensional paradigm. The third dimension makes you believe that you are defined by labels. For example, we are given labels like, "You are Susan from Alabama who went to Auburn University and teach at Central High School."

The third dimension operates from a competition and scarcity mindset causing you to embrace a distorted belief system. You then become a slave to the labels that have been placed on you that are then perpetuated through the news and social media. All of these things and more are third dimensional mindsets. These are traps and chains that are put on us, and because we don't know any better, we embrace them. This was why I had to leave Indiana. I was getting caught up in the labels that were beginning to define me. I was Derek the basketball player, the business owner, the OneLife sports gear CEO, the father, the partner, the weird guy, the (fill in the blank with whatever the world uses to define us). I was being crushed under those labels, so I had to leave in order to redefine my paradigm. And choosing to leave the third dimension opened up my life for the fifth dimensional paradigm shift to begin.

In the fifth dimension, there is an awareness point that you are not the body. You have a body, but you understand that you are not your body. You are attached to nothing but connected to everything. You are aware that you are creating at all times. You understand that there is no such thing as separation. We are all connected. And the foundational truth of the fifth dimension is love. Love is the only thing that exists. You don't attach yourself to anything else but that truth. It is an awareness of complete oneness and the fact that we are projecting ourselves into everything we see around us.

When you find yourself shifting into the fifth dimension, you will begin to consistently peel back the layers that have been placed on you. It is a place of constant evolvement. At the same time, living in this dimension is the hardest thing you will ever have to do because you truly understand who you are. It's both a blessing and a curse. The blessing is you can actually play the game of life without getting caught up in the game. The curse is once your eyes have been open, your heart will be broken. You will see the illusion and the way everyone around you is falling into the trap.

If these concepts seem complex and completely counter intuitive to what you have been taught to embrace, it's because they are. The movement from the third to the fifth dimension is not an easy one. In fact, like I said above, it is probably one of the most difficult things you will ever embark upon. So, this journey is not for everyone. Some people find comfort in the third dimension and don't really want to leave. That's fine. I'm not here to force my beliefs or lifestyle on anyone. However, to the ones who are hungry for a shift in their lives, I'm here to give you the information and allow you to do with it as you will. Your hunger for growth and desire to experience something different brought you here. Now it's up to you to decide what you want to do with it.

This book is set up in a way to simplify what may be considered complex information by breaking up the concepts into four different sections: mind, physical, nutrition, and environment. Underneath each section are the areas that are required to live in the fifth dimension. For each concept, the challenge will always be application. But as you apply, you will start to see changes occur. And I want to warn you, one of the most difficult aspects of growth is the pushback you may receive from those around you, especially those close to you.

In fact, those you call family can become the worst people in the transition from the third to the fifth dimension because of the loyalty you feel towards them and your desire to be accepted. Your family may struggle understanding your decisions that go against the norm. But if you are trying to be accepted, your family will usually be the ones that lock you down to the third dimensional frame of mind because they don't want you to change. I'm not going to tell you how to deal with this, but you have to choose who is most important - you or the people around you. You have to decide whose opinion matters the most - yours or those supposedly close to you. You have to decide how you want to live your life - for yourself or for everyone else.

Section 1

Mind

Chapter 2

Imagination/Vision

Vision and imagination are paramount to a fifth dimension mindset. In fact, they are foundational principles. But to fully understand the power of vision and imagination, I need you to go back to your childhood first - to a time when your vision and imagination were operating at their peak. No one had to tell you to use your imagination or to get a vision of who you wanted to be. When you were a kid, all you did was use your imagination. A tree wasn't just a tree; it was a fortress. A stick wasn't just a stick; it was a sword. A cardboard box wasn't just a box; it was a home.

As kids, we lived in a world of endless possibilities where nothing was impossible. And to really understand the fifth dimension, you have to approach it with the same awe and wonder as you did when you were a child. There is a passage from the Bible that says, unless you become like a child, you can't enter the kingdom. This statement carries so much weight in the process of your journey from the third to fifth dimension. Our minds have been fucked by so many systems, so to reclaim our minds, we've got to go back.

Think about it. You don't have to teach a young kid to believe in themselves because doubt doesn't exist in their minds. Kids can see something that doesn't exist and believe wholeheartedly that it is real. Kids naturally have creative imagination. In fact, I can tell a kid right now, "Why don't you write me a book," and without reservation, he will write it by tomorrow. I actually challenged my younger son with this same task. He has always been creative, so one day I told him I would give him $100 if he wrote a book. Right after I gave him the challenge I thought, "Man, there is no way he's going to write a book." But literally the next day, he brought me a whole book. He had drawn animals on lined paper and wrote words on the bottom of the pages. He stapled the pages together and handed it over to me with pride. I was stunned because if I had challenged an adult to do the same thing, he would have immediately grappled with doubts and fears, causing him to procrastinate because deep down he really wouldn't think he could do it. Kids don't have those types of beliefs injected into them yet.

Kids can see beyond "reality." They might draw a picture that looks like scribble to us, but to them it looks like a dragon, a unicorn, or a castle. I remember when I was younger, I had a best friend named Ralph who I hung out with every single day. Ralph was my dude. When I would be at the house by myself, it would be me and Ralph. We used to hang. I talked to him, and he talked to me.

The only catch was, Ralph wasn't "real." He was my imaginary friend, but at that age, there was no way you could tell me he wasn't real. I actively engaged with Ralph and knew exactly what he looked and sounded like. He was real to me no matter what people around me said.

I'm sure each of you could tell similar stories from your childhood. From imaginary friends to made up games, our imagination was what made the world around us come to life. It was what made life an adventure. But then, our imagination and vision were demonized. They were labeled as "childish" and something to "grow out of." And just like that, the system starts to fuck us up. At a young age, the slow systematic removal of our power in the form of our imagination and vision begins. And one of the major culprits is the school system.

The school system tries to construct our minds to receive programmed information, and we get a fucking grade to regurgitate that information. So, our minds get flooded with useless fucking data. And the better you are with regurgitating data, the better grades you get. The kids with a more vivid imagination get D's and F's because they don't just want to hold on to useless data. Then these same kids go home and get a slap on the wrist or paddled because they refuse to submit to the programming from the system. But others get a "good job, Johnny" for getting all A's and affirmation and validation from teachers, principals, and family. The reward of school comes with being able to robotically morph into structured beliefs that fit a larger narrative within society. The kids that are still trying to hold on to their creative imagination are punished by the school system because they struggle with regurgitation. "Learning" is then minimized to listening, following directions, receiving the information you are fed without questioning, and letting go of "childish" behavior that is really just independent thinking.

Your family system can be just as damaging as the school system. When you are born into this reality, you come with the need to be validated and appreciated by your parents. You want them to be proud of you, but they've already been so conditioned by the system that they in turn train you under that same system. They think in order for you to be "good," you have to follow the rules, get good grades, go to school, get a job, dress a certain way, have beliefs that align with what we are being fed by the media, etc. Your parents have conformed to the system and want you to conform as well, making them an integral part of this controlled process.

As a parent, I have been guilty of this as well. Even with how much I'm evolving, growing and learning, I can still mistakenly parent my kids from a space of judgement as opposed to cultivating their imagination. When I had challenged my younger son to write a book and he brought me the stapled lined papers, I dismissed his efforts. I said, "Man, that ain't no book. I'm talkin' about a *real* book." And to see his face go south because he was so proud to show me that book still brings me feelings of regret and guilt to this day. Who was I to discredit his creation? I was trying to tell him what a real book was while he was presenting to me the book he created. I withheld my validation because I was basing my response on what the system told me was a *real* book instead of allowing my son to create his own version of a book. I'm sure we've all had those experiences where our imagination came alive but the system or people within the system condemned us or redirected us towards control instead of freedom.

The truth is, every system is structured intentionally to fuck us up because if people knew the power of their mind, we wouldn't need the mind control from systems (the school system, the political system, FDA, family system, etc.). We would realize that we can create our realities through vision and imagination as we go because consciousness is the creator of reality. Instead of allowing systems to tell us what to think, we can create the world we live in. We wouldn't have to judge things by applying labels. Instead, we could allow things to open themselves up to us and tell us what and who they are. Let me explain this further.

We are surrounded by all this magic everyday - but we demystify it by giving everything labels. We say, "Oh that's just a tree; that's just a chair; that's just a this or that." But, when you put a label on something, you put chains on it in your own mind. However, if you don't label, you would open your mind to the environment around you and realize that *everything* is speaking to you because *everything* is alive. Once again, this concept shouldn't seem foreign to you because there was a time when this was true for you. You just didn't realize it then.

Remember a time when you didn't just look at your bed and label it as a "bed." As a child, you let it come alive. You let it speak to you and saw it as whatever the fuck your imagination wanted it to be. As a child, you took the chains off of the third dimension and let it operate in the fifth dimension.

When you lock your mind down with labels, you take away its ability to create. However, when you look at the world without judgement or labels, the world becomes alive. The environment around you is then able to speak to you and you become the creator instead of the mere character.

The question now is, how do we reclaim our vision and imagination? The good news is we don't have to reach outside of ourselves. It is already within us. Everything in the Universe is mental. All is mind. So, the first step is to activate your vision. Get a vision in your mind of who you want to be, how you want to look, how you want your body to perform, and any other desire you have for yourself. Write it down every day. Get so clear with that vision and you will start to attract everything you need to become what you see in your mind.

This happens in nature. A watermelon seed is just a seed, but the mind of a watermelon seed wants to be a watermelon. So, it attracts the nutrients, sunlight and everything else it needs in its environment for the expression of the watermelon to be seen in the third dimension. The same is true for us. It all starts with a seed, and the most fertile ground in the Universe is the human mind. Since everyone's mind is fertile, the question you must ask yourself is, what is my mind fertile for?

We have been plugged into a system, a matrix, whatever you want to call it, and it has injected us with the beliefs it wants us to have. This means our minds have become fertile for whatever is being planted by the system, and we reap a harvest of everyone else's beliefs. Our reality is then a creation not of our making. But we don't have to surrender to this. We are the true creators of our reality if we want to be.

We are the creators, but instead of creating, we replay and recreate all the things that have been put inside of us. Our minds have been sabotaged with the agendas of "them," "the elite" or the people holding the strings of the matrix. We have the power to choose what to put into our minds, but instead we surrender our power and allow our minds to be planted with everyone else's ideas and beliefs. That's why TV, music, movies and other forms of media are so powerful because the people running those media channels can inject the vision and ideas they want to accomplish into the minds of the consumer. And because we don't understand the power of our minds, we passively receive like robots. We replace our imagination with a third dimensional reality and low vibrational belief systems in the form of labels, and we get stuck into a belief system that was placed upon us. Then, we no longer even attempt to create our reality anymore. We just fall in line - literally, we fall in line. And we minimize our existence to labels - I'm from this city; I'm a fan of this team; I go to this school; I eat at this restaurant. Just like that, we allow the outside world to define us. We get defined rather than doing the defining.

But to start to reclaim our minds, it takes someone like me and you to say, "Nah, motherfucker. I'm taking my mind back. I'm about to create the reality that I want to create. I'm about to put what I want into my mind. I'm gonna write my goals down. I'm gonna visualize what I want to visualize." At the same time, you have to keep anything out of your fucking reality that doesn't cultivate or encourage your vision and imagination. Doubts, fears, disbelief, and discouragement are like weeds, rodents, and hyenas to your mind.

Just know that taking back the power of your mind can be hard. The creators are demonized and called Satan, crazy, weird, deceived, etc. But despite the pushback, having your own vision is paramount to becoming your greatest self. And starting with a vision of who you want to be and holding on to that vision no matter what will attract the people, places, and things into your life to make that a reality. It unlocks the world around you and gives you permission to imagine again.

In this book we are talking about having an infinite mind, which is centered around your imagination. As Albert Einstein says, "Imagination is everything. It is the preview of coming events. Imagination embraces the entire world, stimulating progress, giving birth to evolution."

When I was a high school basketball player, I had a ritual I would do. The day before every game, I would sit in my reclining chair, lean back and listen to the R. Kelly song "I Can't Sleep Baby." As I sat in the chair, I would close my eyes and play the entire game in my mind before I played the game on the court. I would vividly picture my movements up and down the court along with my opponents' counter moves. And on the day of the game, I would walk onto the court with complete confidence because in my mind, I had already played the game. I was two, three, and four steps ahead of everyone. And for me to be 6'3" and lead the whole city and state in rebounding meant that I knew where the ball was going before it came off the rim. Think about that for a minute. I was playing in the basketball capital of the world against all these 6'9", 6'10", and 7'0" opponents, and I'm 6'3" leading these other rebounders because I played the game in my mind before I played against any of them on the court. That's how powerful imagination is.

Do you want to tap into the power of your imagination again? Shift your focus and realize that from this day on, you have a magic genie that can create anything you want in your reality. With that magic genie, you can ask, be and have anything you can ever dream is possible. The problem is we don't even realize this genie exists because we have been taught to think so small. But the good news is you can recapture your imagination.

Your imagination is like a muscle, and just like every muscle in your body, it must be strengthened, built, and worked. Start conditioning that muscle by setting a timer for five minutes every day, close your eyes and simply imagine. If you had no limitation and all the money in the world, what would your life look like; what would you be doing; what would your body look like? Imagine it. As you make this a daily practice, you will see that muscle grow and build, and five minutes will no longer be enough. You will want to keep imagining because you will start seeing the world around you come to life. The more you get in alignment with who you really are, you will attract thoughts from another place. You will start to pick up on a different frequency, and imagination will be easier because you will be able to co-create with your higher self. That co-creation will bring what you really want from the fifth dimension down to this planet.

People with atrophied imagination muscles will have a hard time with this. If you don't want to work your imagination muscle, someone is going to create your reality for you. If you aren't creating, you are being created. Either you are using science, or someone is using science on you. It's the same with someone who has atrophied muscles who becomes solely dependent on a wheelchair or a caregiver. No longer able to move without assistance, they become a slave to the motives and intentions of someone or something else. This passive existence can be comfortable, which is why some people just want to be fed into the system. They don't want to know the truth, nor do they want to unplug. If that's the case, they will forever be a slave to the physical reality of the third dimension. While using your imagination is more difficult, the end result is freedom.

The truth is you really aren't your body. What you are is a fucking powerful being that is abundant, prosperous, fun, creative - all the things you really, truly desire to be - you are that. You just have to uncover all the lies and controlled beliefs that keep you from that. Get away from labels and allow things to be what they are without you putting chains around them. Really seek first to understand before you put your understanding on something. Ask the things and people around you what they are before you define them through limiting labels. Come from a place of intrigue and wonder. Instead of thinking you know some shit, realize you don't know anything and turn everything into wonder again. Just experience this game and get back to being more of an observer. And as you apply this to the world around you, you can't help but start approaching yourself with that same wonder. Take off your own labels and start asking yourself who you really are. For those of you going through a difficult transition or you feel the growing pains from another life transition, know that this is the best time to lean into your imagination. When we face the uncertainty of life, it is an opportunity to use our imagination to create something new. Let your imagination guide you not your fears, apathy, or the opinions of others.

An exercise that you can do every day is to take five minutes and write down what you are creating from your imagination. Research says that writing on white paper in blue ink connects your words more to your brain and emotions, which allows it to become more carved in your imagination. Write without stopping or second guessing yourself.

Chapter 3
Beliefs

Now that we've established the power of your vision and imagination, we must align this with your beliefs because whether you want to embrace this revelation or not, the truth is, we've been spoon fed our beliefs since infancy. And our beliefs are intentionally connected to the labels we've been given, which then determines our reality.

If your imagination is the creator and you have a magic genie, obviously that is going to shift your perception of reality. And as we touch on each concept in this section, you will find yourself working on all of them simultaneously. That is the nature of mind work - it all works concurrently. The concepts may sound redundant, but just remember that as you alter one, the others will follow because they are interconnected.

So, since we are still focusing on creating your own reality, and with the knowledge that everything you believe has been handed to you at birth, your current reality has most likely been built on the foundation of someone else's beliefs. Think about that for a minute. Your reality is not one of your making. It was made for you.

Let's say that you were raised to believe that the people around you are racist. Then, everything in your world will respond to that belief. Your surroundings will serve to affirm that belief. But, if you were raised to believe that the world is loving and accepting, your reality will bring that belief to life. Interestingly enough, those contradictory belief systems can survive under the same conditions, in the same area and yet operate as two completely different realities for the people embracing those belief systems.

Your beliefs are creating your reality at every second, and up until this point, everything you have been creating has been pummeled into your subconscious mind. You are then replaying those beliefs because the third dimension is merely a replay of what's going on in your subconscious. That's why the third dimension is the slowest form of creation.

This is true for every one of the beliefs you have been given. For example, the beliefs I was given were - I am a body; I am defined by my name and place of birth; the color of my skin matters; success is defined by what you possess - and the list can go on. These beliefs became subconscious and dictated the way I dealt with other people and the way I operated in the world. Our beliefs are what separate us and create a reality that allows us to be easily manipulated and controlled. The beliefs that we have been assigned keep us in an ego-centric mindset and put us in a "I vs. them" mentality. Then, the media and the "powers that be" are able to utilize those beliefs to sway our decisions. So, if I identify as my body, as my name, as my hometown, etc., then I will establish beliefs that are unique to that label. Think about the power behind that. This is why the motive behind most of what is fed to us is based on controlling our minds. And once those beliefs are implanted, we then become a slave to the emotions and habits that arise from these labels attached to our beliefs.

I'm sure we could spend time unpacking the beliefs you currently hold and the origin of those beliefs, but it would be a waste of time. Altering your beliefs starts by answering this simple question: what the fuck do you want to believe? The answer to this question has the power to alter everything around you because if you alter your beliefs, the reality around you completely changes. So, using the example from above, if you change your belief that everyone around you is racist to the belief that everyone around you is unconditionally loving, then not only do you change, but the world around you changes as well.

The phrase, "limiting beliefs" gets thrown around a lot in the self-help world. If you think you have limiting beliefs, then you don't understand fifth dimensional thinking. You're basing your life on what you have been told by the guru on TV at 5 o'clock in the morning who's trying to get you to buy her book.

Here's the truth. There is no such thing as limiting beliefs because *all* beliefs have power. People label beliefs as "limiting," "good," or "bad," but that shit just doesn't exist. All beliefs just are, and categorizing beliefs is based on subjectivity. If your belief is good for you, then it's good for you. It might be a shitty belief for me, but if it works for you, then it's for you. The key is connecting to the power of the belief and not the man-made categories of that belief. Really grasping this concept requires awareness that your beliefs are creating your reality and you have the power to change your reality by changing your beliefs. Those beliefs can either give you the power to be the creator or enslave you to become the creation. In fact, until you are locked into the fifth dimension, you will always be the fucking slave. You will always be the victim and the effect to someone else's cause. But in the fifth dimension, you are a thought leader. You are a pioneer. You are no longer subject to others' beliefs. You are the belief. You are the spark. You are the mother fucking master, omega, everything. You are captain of your ship.

To hold that type of frequency takes courage and work because everything around you is trying to get you to let go of that frequency. And the person you will have to battle with the most is yourself because our default is to love the belief that we are being oppressed, victimized, and controlled. This belief system will never cause me to accept any personal responsibility. It will always be about something or someone else.

Believing and becoming the alpha, the spark, the cause, GOD -- means you must trace all the effects back to the cause

-- and the cause will always be you. You are the causation, and everything in your reality exists in your belief system first. When you understand this, you realize you created your wife cheating on you; you created someone that cut you off in traffic; you created your money problems. It all comes back to you. This is all awareness. When you believe that you are the creator of your reality, it takes away from the trauma or guilt that is associated with any life event. You realize that you aren't being punished by the Universe, another person, the government, the economy or anything outside yourself. In fact, nothing outside of you is trying to destroy you. They don't have that kind of power - only you do.

Now that we know that anything you believe will solidify your reality and that you are the master and creator, it is time to choose to believe whatever the fuck you want. Here's some strategies you can use as your starting point.

1. <u>Results Over Charisma</u> - Never listen to anyone in any field that is not experiencing the results you want to produce. You should repeat this to yourself every day. Everybody has an opinion and belief on how shit gets done and what is best for you. But if they aren't experiencing what you want to produce, you should never, ever listen to them because their beliefs are fucking wrong. Don't let anyone create your reality with their slavish belief systems that were handed to them over and over again, especially when you start to take ownership of your life. Even if they make it sound good.

Look at the results of their life to determine how effective their beliefs really are.

2. Establish Core Beliefs - The only way to change your beliefs is to become aware of what you believe. Then get rid of the beliefs that don't serve you and align the rest with these core beliefs:

   I create my own reality.

   What I think I become.

   Everything that happens in my reality, I create.

3. Your Process is Unique - The process of changing your beliefs is different for everyone. You must first become aware of your beliefs and work to change them, which will look different for everyone.

4. Never Ending Battle - Changing your beliefs will be the hardest fight of your life, and it is infinite. If you think about it, from the moment we get out of bed in the morning, other people, society, social media, etc. bombard us with their belief systems. This means that living in the fifth dimension requires awareness and intentionality every day, and it won't be easy.

If you are ready to change your beliefs, ask yourself the question that's been repeated in this chapter at the beginning of each day: "What the fuck do I want to believe today?" And when you answer that question, trust that your reality and the Universe around you will mirror those beliefs you chose to embrace and proclaim.

Chapter 4

Thoughts

Beliefs are deeply rooted into your makeup and your creation, so another step in changing these and moving into the fifth dimension is through your thoughts. When you are activating your imagination and beliefs, you are thinking. And as you think, you are creating; and as you create and continue to think, your beliefs turn to thoughts, thoughts turn to reality, and reality becomes a pattern that allows you to create the world you want to live in. When you proclaim what your unique beliefs are, you then have to align your thoughts with those beliefs. When you choose what you want to believe, you've already sparked a whole new wave of light and possibilities. A whole new Universe just opened up. And when you incorporate thoughts into this new Universe, your thoughts become your workers.

Thoughts are spirits. Thoughts are things. We live in a thought Universe, and every thought that you think has a place in your reality. And when you understand how concrete your thoughts are, you will be more cognizant about what you allow into your orbit or auric field. The auric field is a light body and energy vortex that travels four feet around your body. When you let someone into your auric field, you are no longer you. Instead, you are one with them. Knowing this, you shouldn't just let everyone into your auric field because whatever their vibrational state is becomes connected to you. You then pick up on their thoughts, energy, and frequency and make it your own. This is why you must protect your auric field. Since every tiny thought is going to get replayed on the screen of your reality and dictate how you live your life, this field must be protected.

Each one of your thoughts is like gold. The Bible says that wisdom, stemming from our thoughts, is more valuable than rubies and diamonds. Your thoughts are one of the most valuable things you can control, and once you realize that your *mind is all* and there is nothing in this physical form that will even touch the infinite potential of your mind, you will become powerful beyond measure.

As I've said before, going from the third to the fifth is an awareness, but in order to really play, have fun and enjoy your life's experience, you have to know that you're in a game and life is a mere simulation. And the field in which you are playing on is in your mind. Remember that your mind is your garden, and that's where you implant thoughts which produce your reality. Perhaps this is why our school career begins in kindergarten (a kind of garden) when our minds are the most fertile, for that is when thoughts are easily planted and grown into physical manifestations.

When you shift your awareness, you are more careful of the thoughts that are planted in your mind. You take heed to the people that are around you, the books you read, the music you listen to, the relationships you get into, etc. It becomes easier to say, "This motherfucker is talking about some bullshit. Man, I'm out." If you find out someone is talking shit about you, you reject the thought that could grow something detrimental and replace it with powerful thoughts. Instead of thinking, "I am worthless," replace it with "I am worthy." Instead of thinking, "I am living in lack," replace it with, "I am abundance."

Don't embrace anyone's thoughts that aren't coming from you. That's why it is so important to be conscious of your surroundings. I always tell my sons that they have to protect their gates, which are entry ways. You have to protect your mind, your ears, your mouth, your eyes, your auric field, and your tongue. Put guards at your gate to ensure that what is coming in and going out has been protected by the reality you want to create.

Your thoughts are deeply rooted into your make-up and creation, but your thoughts have been hijacked for someone else's creation. And once you realize that your thoughts are literally things and that as you think so you become, then you elevate your awareness concerning the people around you that are imparting thoughts into your mind. The places you go, the media you watch, images you take in, conversations you have, even the environments you allow yourself to be in - your subconscious is taking in all of that information. One trillion times a second, your subconscious is photographing the information and translating it into thoughts.

You have the power to stop the thought patterns running in your mind that aren't serving you. This will actually be one of the hardest battles of your life. Every day, all day, we are being led like sheep to the slaughter. Our thoughts and our collective consciousness are being consumed by others. Social media, the government, the news media, the school system, etc. are all living off of our energy because they are feeding us the thoughts that keep us stuck and dead inside. We are so stuck in a parasitical, sick, diseased, dependent mindset that is fed through the thoughts we have been given.

Here are some strategies you can use as often as possible to take control of your thoughts:

1. <u>Awareness</u> - The most important step is to stop thinking and focus on your breathing. As you focus on your breathing, you are then in a space to become aware that thoughts are things. They are your workers. So, when your mind is clear, you are able to choose the thoughts you want to send out into the universe to do the work you are assigning them. As you think, so you are, which is why

awareness is key to creating the thoughts that determine who you are and direct the Universe around you.

2. Holding Your Thoughts - The book "Think and Grow Rich" by Napoleon Hill was published in 1937 after the author spent twenty years following the most wealthy and successful people on the planet. The assignment was for him to figure out the strategies and secrets that these people used to bring them to their current level of success. From his research, he identified the law of success in 16 lessons. In fact, that was the initial title of the book - "The Law of Success in 16 Lessons." The problem was, when the book came out, the super wealthy read it and said, "Nah, you're giving up too much information," so Napoleon had to take out all the pieces that they didn't want the masses to know about. And what was left is now found in the book, "Think and Grow Rich."

The concept of holding a thought is actually one of the laws from the 16 lessons Napoleon wrote about. The idea behind this is, if you hold a thought for 17 seconds in your mind, it is equivalent to 2,000 hours in physical work. If you hold a thought for 34 seconds, it is equivalent to 200,000 hours in work. If you hold a thought for 51 seconds, it is equivalent to 2 million hours of work. And 68 seconds of holding a thought is the magic number since it equals an infinite number of hours on the physical dimension of work. The lesson here is, instead of thinking that your ass needs to be out here grinding for 15 hours a day, work on the inside and the unseen realm of your thoughts because that's where creation starts.

Once the thought comes down here in the third dimensional form, it is at the slowest form of creation. What you are seeing with your eyes is vibrating so slowly, which is why you can see it. Everything you see is a thought. That's why I can create my body. I'm holding a thought about my body, which sends my thoughts or workers forth, and what results is the physical manifestation of my thought in the third dimension. This translates into the body I created in the fifth dimension.

This can be applied to every other area of your life. If you are thinking of starting a business, before you make a business plan or apply for a fucking loan, get good at relaxing and holding thoughts because that's what is going to be the most valuable for you and yield the best results.

3. <u>Monitor Your Environment</u> – Best-selling author and motivational speaker, Jim Rohn says you are the average of the 5 people you hang around. Like I said earlier, when someone comes into your auric field, you become one with that person. There is a story that illustrates this point and it's about a man named Aristotle Onassis who was the richest man on the planet. One day someone asked him, "If you lost all your money, what would you do?" Aristotle answered, "If I lost all my money, all I would do is go to where the

wealthiest people are and sit amongst them. And just from being in that environment, money will come to me so fast because those thoughts will rub off on me."

Aristotle knew what you are learning right now, which is that thoughts are paramount and determine your overall success. You want to be in shape? Take your ass to where the most fit people in the world are at. You want to be an accountant? Go to where the accountants are meeting at. You want to be an actress? Go to Hollywood. If you want to be a successful whatever, go around where those successful whatevers are at. Thoughts rub off as you become one with those in your auric field, so you must be calculated with who you allow into your thought world. It's another tool in your tool belt to create the reality you want to create.

4. <u>Get the Fuck Out -</u> When I decided to leave my environment in Indianapolis, Indiana and travel across the country without any solid plans, it seemed drastic to those around me at the time. But as I was becoming more aware of mindset work, transformative teachings and new knowledge, I could see how the environment around me was hindering my growth. It's like the common metaphor of the crabs in a bucket. All the crabs in the bucket know they are trapped, but if there is the potential for one of the crabs to escape, collectively the group won't let it escape. It's the "If I can't have it, neither can you," mentality.

I knew I had to get out when I could see that the negative energy around me was trying to overpower my new beliefs and new understanding. It wasn't until I physically ejected myself from that environment that I was free to really construct the reality I wanted to live in. It was like crossing over a bridge of enlightenment. My level of awareness caused me to leave everything behind for my own salvation. And the same must be true for you. You almost have to be willing to die for your own truth. I was then, and I still am willing to die for my truth now. It's not worth it to me to live in somebody else's dream. My soul isn't built like that. Your moves may seem drastic as your level of awareness grows, but if that is what you need to do, then do it without apology.

Chapter 5
Focus and Meditation

From the first three chapters, you've seen that once you realize that *you* have the power, and *you* are the creator (always have been, always will be), you will then begin to tune your thoughts to focus on where you want to be and who you want to be. You will no longer be derailed by your thoughts. Instead, you will focus on the thoughts of your choosing and build upon them. You will start to become aware of what you believe in, what you see, and how you've been in a reactive state instead of a focused state. One of the best ways to do this is through the practice of meditation and focus.

Meditation is becoming aware and stepping back from life to see it from a higher level and vantage point. It allows you to observe what you are thinking, how you are breathing and how your organs are feeling. It gives you a bird's eye view with what the fuck is going on inside of you. And like I said in previous chapters, our mind is like a garden, so meditation gives you the opportunity to identify what you are growing in that garden.

Focus is tuning in to what you want to believe. It asks the question, "What do I want to grow in my garden?" Through meditation, you realize what's going on with your mind and where your thoughts are going. Then, you tune your focus into what you want to grow. That's why gratitude, looking for the good, and knowing what the fuck you want is so important. Because once you align your focus to those things and stop giving it away to TV, news, social media, sex, and all these other things that are vying for your attention, only the things that are a vibrational match will show up on the screen of your reality. Meaning, whatever you focus on grows. Quantum physics says, until you focus on something, it doesn't exist. When you understand that nothing even fucking exists until you focus on it, you will only focus on that which will benefit your reality and give up anything that's not tuned into your universe.

Let's look at meditation first to understand the simple step of awareness. When people talk about meditation, the image of someone sitting on the ground with their legs crossed and eyes closed probably comes to mind. While this is a form of meditation, the act of meditating is simply being aware of your breath and your "self" beyond your physical body. Lying down, focusing on your breath, and closing your eyes are ways to get into that state.

As you slow your breath, you are able to slow your world, control matter and create space between the third and fifth dimension. When you are in this state, you are unattached to this dimension and are no longer creating from the third dimension. You are now creating from the fifth. This is what is referred to as being "in the zone" or in "flow." Many high-performance athletes like Michael Jordan and Steph Curry get in their zone. This is why they can hit every shot. They are ahead of the matrix because they are in a meditative state and have found their flow. Some people have learned to live life in that state or a fifth dimensional perspective.

When life is in flow, you are living in a meditative state. That's the goal of meditation itself -- slowing your breath to master a meditative state and high level of consciousness and awareness. Meditation is the detaching from yourself so you can see yourself outside of yourself to determine what you need to focus on. It allows you to get back into you and into your seat. Meditation allows you to separate from those attachments around you (your name, your body, your income, your labels, etc.) and tune into who you really are.

Once you tune in to who you are, you will start to think, "I've been in someone else's dream of reality." Meditation allows you to sit back in the driver's seat because right now most people are passive passengers while living in someone else's mind. Let me explain further. Everything in this universe is a thought, and those thoughts trickle down into the third dimension. As we think, we create. The chair I'm sitting in right now, the room I'm sitting in, all of it was once in someone's mind. So, I'm literally living in someone else's mind right now.

Most people are living and existing in other people's minds, not realizing they are supposed to be the creator of their dreams and the builder of their own lives. But they are so distracted and weak that they don't know they have the power to create. They give their power away when they give their focus away and stay locked into the third dimension. And being a third dimensional being is so far from who we were meant to be. The third dimension - eating, sex, watching TV, phones - all of it keeps us locked down in a third dimensional state.

Most of us need to shut down the many distractions competing for our attention. We need to turn our phones off, turn meditation music on, lie down, focus on our breath, and become aware of our thoughts so we can figure out what's really going on in our minds. When meditation starts becoming a regular practice, you can then start to live in a constant meditative state.

You'll know you are moving from taking a moment to meditate to an actual meditative state when you start consistently feeling good. When you are generally happy; synchronistic events are taking place; you are no longer in your head and overthinking; you are having fun with this reality; and you are in a creative space -- that's when you know you are resting in a meditative state. You will know you are in that state because it will feel like you are flowing with life. Time will become a secondary thought, and when you come out of that state, you will think, "Damn, I really was in a meditative state." Many people use drugs to get in that state, "to see under the veil," so to speak. But that's actually our natural birth right, and you can access it by starting with these steps.

1. Become aware of your body - This will be tough for a lot of people because when you are used to so many distractions, it can be difficult to simply be with your body. Remember that you are the awareness that is in control of your body.

2. Become aware of your breath - Breath is literally Spirit passing through you. The longer and deeper you breathe, the more this reality slows down. Your mind will slow down, and you will be able to take a bird's eye view with what's going on inside of you. After you slow your breath, you are able to slow the creation process because you can see the pictures going on in your mind. You are then able to shift the pictures and create what you want to see in this reality

3. Do what you love to do - When you are doing what you love to do, it's easy to escape and exit this matrix because you are able to be a kid again. You are able to be free and express yourself as a creative being. Athletes, artists, writers, skaters, musicians, and dancers get in a meditative state frequently because they are doing what they love to do. They stop thinking and just create. The more you do that, the more you will unconsciously get in that state. Do anything that's going to allow you to enjoy the moment and have fun - go for a walk on the beach, yoga, dance, paint, sing - whatever it is. It's really about being in the moment and being present. When you are in the moment, that is basically meditation.

Once you do these things, you will merge the third dimension with the fifth and your higher self will tell you what to focus on. You will be guided to what your higher self wants. The more you get in that middle space, the more you can separate yourself from getting bogged down in this dimension and being trapped with what is going on in your mind. That takes you back to focus. Once you become aware of what's going on in your mind, then you can pick out what you want to focus on.

Everyone has a purpose. We are all designed for something, and once you realize what you are designed for, you will no longer want to be distracted by bullshit. You won't want to go out drinking, smoking, and hanging with people who are vibrating at a low frequency. You will want to spend your time doing what you are designed to do. Focus becomes easier when you embrace the fact that you are different, and the people around you will not understand the frequency you are on. You will have to turn your self-love all the way up. And you are going to have to face and overcome so many fears, demons, and patterns of existing that no longer serve you.

But even after you become aware and know what your purpose is, the battle is going to be forever. The people that run the third dimension don't want you to wake up to who you are because then you are no longer a resource for them to use. Right now, your mind and consciousness are being used for their reality. And when you unplug from their matrix, you are no longer useful to them. Everyone around you will want you to stay plugged in. If they are plugged in, they want you to plug in. They'll ask you, "What are we doing tonight; what are we watching tonight; what are we smoking; what are we drinking?"

Remember, your focus is your ultimate superpower. It is literally magic. If you don't give something focus, it doesn't exist. That is your power source. It's really simple, so don't over complicate it. Your focus will then attract more thoughts that are in line with the pattern you choose. As you are learning to focus in general, focus on breathing first. Then, focus on feeling good, being grateful, enjoying life, doing what you love to do, being aware of your thoughts and understanding who you are.

As you continue to meditate and focus, anything that you discover that is not serving your greatest good and highest self, cut it out. We all have a tuning mechanism inside of us that acts like a radar, which is our intuition. And when you are paying attention to it, your intuition will pick up on any and everything that's not supposed to be in your garden. If a coyote or squirrel comes into your garden, you've got to get that motherfucker out of there. I don't care how cute the distraction is; it/he/she has to go.

Section 2
Physical

Chapter 6

Choose Wisely

There is an infinite amount of knowledge, research, and information when it comes to physical fitness. But behind all of it is a slanted perspective used to fund a particular organization because in the end, it's all about the money. This is why it's so important for you to be very conscious about who you listen to. So many people and organizations have an idea or philosophy when it comes to fitness and think that if you don't believe what they believe, then you are wrong. In this world alone, there are countless opinions floating around about physical fitness and health being disguised as facts. However, most of what is embraced in the fitness world and in the Universe in general is just someone's opinion.

The people behind the messaging may not be malicious. In fact, many people have good intentions, but what works for someone may not work for someone else. In fitness, you've got to be careful who you listen to because there is so much money in this, which attracts opinion leaders who have saturated this market with their own belief systems. It's tragic because the person with enough marketing dollars can take an opinion and make it look like a fact in this reality. And it happens over and over again.

The physical fitness industry is eerily similar to religion where money, fear, and control can turn any opinion and make it look like a fact. Like religion, the more people hold on to those opinions disguised as facts, the more it becomes easier to brainwash the minds of people to believe whatever it is the leader or influencer wants them to believe. This has happened century after century as people continue to write books, create courses and make money off of these belief systems, and they continue to perpetuate the same loop of information. Now, we have a whole culture of people who have been brought up with a specific fitness mentality and belief system in their DNA, which controls their paradigm in the way they see the world and how they operate in this reality.

It takes someone like me and other pioneers to shift and really unplug people from the physical fitness belief systems that aren't fucking working. Think about this. If religion was really working, then people wouldn't be walking around deaf, dumb and blind to reality. People would stop returning to the same church building seeking a cure to the same problems that brought them there in the first place. They would realize that they are infinite beings, their thoughts are powerful, and their bodies are temples. They would be more conscious about how they use their energy and how their frequency works. Going to church is like a hospital for sick people that are looking for a cure but are leaving with placebos that feel good but illicit no real change. Because if real change was happening, they wouldn't have to be in the hospital every weekend.

The same is true with fitness. If the philosophies of the physical fitness world were working, then we wouldn't be seeing a steady increase in the amount of young people suffering from knee surgeries, the increasing amount of overweight people, and the rising number of really well-meaning people with broken down bodies. In religion, people are well meaning. They have a heart to learn and know God, but they are receiving misguided opinions that are leading them away from God. In fitness, people go to the gym every day and are on the newest diet, but they can't lose weight. They are trying to get a 6-pack with a sculpted body while still keeping their strength, but their body is plagued with constant injuries. Year after year they get so discouraged because the information they are getting is not fucking working. But they are holding on to the hope promised by these "thought leaders." They believe in false promises so much that people are literally willing to sell their souls to these dogmatic teachings. Once this occurs, people then shut their minds off to any other teachings that may challenge what they hold as "truth."

At 43 years old, I've lived through the dogma and belief systems in both the fitness industry and the religious world, and I can honestly say that everything is based on opinion. This can be a discouraging assertion. You might find out that Santa Claus isn't real, the tooth fairy is your mom and dad, and Jesus isn't who you thought he was. Those might be hard pills to swallow until you shift your paradigm and filter the voices you allow to influence your life. The rule I live by, and I encourage others to do the same, is never listen to anyone in any field that is not experiencing the results you want to produce. You will see this again as we move further through the book because it applies to so many other areas of your life. But in this case, you have to assess those you've been listening to in the fitness industry, even if they've labeled themselves as experts in the field.

Reality becomes easier to accept when you understand that the motive behind the miseducation in the fitness industry is control, manipulation, and ultimately money. If you are an orthopedic surgeon and you have 12 knee surgeries every week that's netting you $6 Million every year, why would you want to challenge the message? If you're a part of Big Pharma and there is an incline of scripts written for pain killers, then it would negatively impact your bottom line to preach any other message than what is already out there. There are so many other players in this fitness game as well who are benefiting from the miseducation to include doctors, massage therapists, chiropractors, fitness trainers, surgeons, etc. There are so many levels to this chain of power, so why would they fix something that isn't broken for them? If I was a part of that chain, I wouldn't want to be exposed and neither would you.

The name of the game in the third dimension is power, control, money, and greed. More, more, more - manipulate, dominate and control - these are the building blocks of the third dimension. And the most damaging teachings in the fitness world that people embrace and build their beliefs around are the main parts of manipulation and control. While there are many teachings, here are two that are widely accepted and causing more harm than good:

1. Cardio Conditioning - The idea that daily cardio is needed for your health isn't true. You don't need to be running every day for 45 minutes to achieve the body you want.

2. Lifting weights - This has led to more injuries than not lifting. Most people are more fluid, athletic and have more dynamic bodies before they enter the weightlifting realm. However, the damage done to the body can completely break it down on a lot of different levels. I was a part of it. We are drawn into this. Our ego wants to look like the people in fitness magazines with bulging muscles and sculpted bodies. These images are used to tell us to do XYZ because this person did those things and got those results, not knowing these people just finished a competition where they were drugged up on testosterone and steroids. All the

water has been flushed from their bodies and the photos have been digitally doctored to make everything pop. But we are still going to listen to them because we've bought into the fairy tale. We have taken the outside vision as truth rather than the internal vision.

The reality of what you will discover as you start to change who you listen to may be dismal, but the shift is simple. Only find people that are experiencing the results you want to produce. Because when you meet these people, they may give you information that sounds totally different than what you were led to believe. It might sound unorthodox at first, but when you figure out who you truly are, you will realize that you need a lot less than you think you do in this physical world. When you are trying to construct the body you want and construct the being you want to create, only listen to people who have been where you have been and have experienced what you are experiencing because those are the only people who have the blueprint for you. If someone has imagined something and is not able to create it, they don't really know. They can talk about it, but they don't really live it. If they can say it but they can't create it, then they don't really know it.

To listen to the right person, first and foremost, you have to decide whether what you are listening to is aligning with where you want to go. You've got to start with this. One thing I tell people is if you really want a good body, the only thing (and this sounds so fucking crazy) you need to do is visualize yourself with that body. Once you do that, the outside world will do everything to make that shit a reality. You are going to run into the right person who is experiencing the results you want to produce, and you will tune into the frequency that matches the vision in your mind. There is no way it can't happen. See the life you want and then go about constructing it. This is step one in the process of listening to the right people. Life will then give you the people, circumstances and information that will be the building blocks you need to construct your vision.

Step two is to write down exactly what you want your body to look like and set goals for yourself. We will talk about my belief system when it comes to physical training later on in the book, but first and foremost, create the vision on paper.

Step three becomes a state of preparation because now that you saw it in your mind and wrote it down, be prepared for downloads. You are the painter of your life, so you have to paint the canvas without anyone coming in with their distorted opinions and perspectives distracting you. As you create, you may get thoughts from different dimensions and different realms. You may hear, "I need you to fast for 30 days;" "I need you to change your career;" "I need you to get rid of your husband/wife;" "I need you to go outside in the sun for 2 hours a day." You have to be so aligned with yourself that you trust the downloads even if they challenge a previously held belief. Either way, you must have the vision and realize you are going to have to change. If you aren't experiencing the results you want to produce, you are going to have to fucking change.

The last step is to become aware of where you are at on the teachability index, which measures how teachable you are. Most people, especially if you are reading this book and want access to me for information, have an index of ten when it comes to their willingness to accept new information. However, on the other side of information is your willingness to change. Your score might be different here. If you are a ten on being teachable, but you are a zero on willingness to change, ten times zero is still a zero, which means you won't see a result. You must be a ten on both. When you have someone that has that score, their life is about to do a massive shift.

Imagine a life in which you are surrounded by people and information that consistently aligns with who you are. The amount of growth and success you would experience will blow your mind. Meanwhile, you will no longer be dependent on any new fad or "research-based" fitness approach, and that is real freedom.

Chapter 7

Range of Strength and Flexibility

To create a healthy, durable body that is indefinitely healthy, you have to possess strength combined with flexibility. Much of fitness can be broken down into two groups of people - the body builders and the yogis. For each group, the belief is that their way of training is superior to the other. And while they may incorporate other ideas into their training, most stay true to their philosophy, which is detrimental to both groups. Yogis focus on strength through length and train for mobility. Body builders focus on aesthetics and train for strength. Both hold tightly to their training styles. But leaning too much into either will create deficiencies. The misconception with body builders is that they don't want to get too flexible because they think they'll lose their athleticism and buoyancy. Meanwhile, they are walking around bound up while their muscles stop becoming useful. It is more about aesthetics than anything. At the same time, yogis don't have the strength of a bodybuilder, which can weaken their bodies over time.

The key isn't in proving which one has more benefits; rather, when you combine these two training styles, you have better athleticism, are more structurally balanced and can prevent injury. Before I learned how to train my body properly, I worked with strength and conditioning coaches in high school and college. What I found was that most athletes train for strength and use stretching for supplemental work or during the warmup. When playing college ball, my conditioning coach made me get bulky and strong, which worked. But at the same time, I didn't have alignment. Yes, I was strong, but I was in constant pain with knee and hip issues *as a teenager*. Before any game, it took me a long time to loosen up my muscles. At 18/19 years old, it would take me and our whole team about 25-30 minutes to warm up because the training had us so bound up. We were kids and struggling to get our bodies moving.

I was icing my knees at 19 years old to get through college. Even more disturbing is the fact that I had to get cortisone shots because my hips were so misaligned. Before every game, I had to drive to a hospital to get those shots. My training neglected flexibility so much so that the decline of my body was quick even at my young age.

When you start to lift heavy, for the first 6 months to a year, you will see results, but after that the decline is so rapid. Your body will self-destruct faster than you could have imagined. You will think, "Damn, when I was 18, I was jumping and running without any issues, and now a few years later, I feel like a fucking old man. Your back will start hurting and the aches and pains throughout your body will limit your athletic ability the older you get.

The combination of range of strength and flexibility are ignored in the fitness arena because it's just another system of control and money. The average cost for a knee replacement surgery is between $30,000-$50,000. That doesn't include the medication and rehabilitation costs that are sure to be a part of the process. Why would they want to stop knee replacements, hip replacements, chiropractic care, back surgeries, etc.? These are multi-million-dollar industries that are profiting off of ignorance and improper training.

To be honest, we don't need to lift weights. We have everything we need inside of us. At 44 years old, I can dunk a basketball, run, and do sprints with zero warm up. If someone chases me right now, I can get up and go without pain. That's how the body was designed. Back in the caveman age, if something was chasing after you, you didn't have time to stretch. You had to get the fuck out of there, which meant your body had to be ready. Range of strength exercises and flexibility will help you keep your body 100% ready. Also, it will restore your body after years of damage from false fitness claims or save you years of deterioration by using this method before you lean heavily into isolated yoga or strength training.

The body should be built from the ground up. Here are a few of the stretches and exercises that everyone should be doing frequently to create a healthy, structurally balanced, athletic, and durable body indefinitely.

A. Plantar Fascia Stretch

This stretch called the Plantar Fascia Stretch is one of the most important stretches for overall health of your body and maximizing your athleticism. Sit in this stretch for 2 min at least 3x a week.

B. Tibialis Stretch

Place half of your feet on a Yoga block and sit in this stretch for 2 min. This stretch will help to take unnecessary pressure off your knees, create mobility in your ankles as well as prevent shin splints.

C. SL Pike Stretch

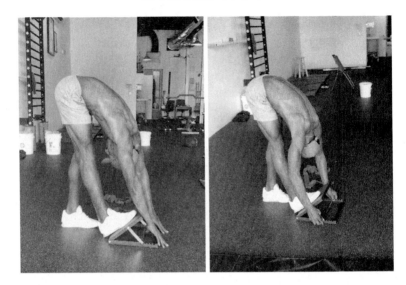

The Posterior Chain (Glutes, hamstrings, low back, and Calves) contribute to 70-75% of overall athleticism. This stretch allows for this most important region of the body to function optimally.

D. Split Squat

This is an exercise that has saved my knees and one of the most important exercises you will ever put in your program. To learn exactly how to perform this exercise correctly, visit my free program for book buyers at Mr1nf1n1ty.com

E. 1nf1n1ty Step Up

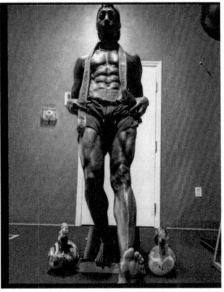

Using a Mr1nf1n1ty VMO board and doing this exercise will build the most important muscle for Knee Longevity (Vastus Medialis Oblique- VMO). You can purchase this VMO Board at Mr1nf1n1ty.com and learn more about this exercise.

F. The Nordic

If you want to be an explosive athlete, protect your knees, and be a step ahead of the competition, the Nordic exercise should be done 2x a week consistently. Learn more at Mr1nf1n1ty.com

These are just some of the many exercises that we are bringing to the forefront of human consciousness to create a happy, healthy, fit, balanced, strong, and flexible body that can play forever. If you are interested in a more comprehensive program that addresses both strength and flexibility, visit Mr1nf1n1ty.com to enroll.

Section 3
Nutrition

Chapter 8

Food is an Addiction

If you want to find the secrets of the universe, think in terms of energy, frequency and vibration. The day science begins to study nonphysical phenomena, it will make more progress in one decade then all the previous centuries of its existence. -Nikola Tesla

"What do you eat? What does your diet look like? How much protein do you eat? What foods do you consume? Are you vegan?" There is not a day that goes by that I don't get asked these question or ones similar. Now that I'm in my 40s, I can confidently say I've experimented with almost every "diet" known to man. I've done vegan, juicing, Paleo, fruit diet, protein shakes, high protein, low starches - no one can tell me something that I haven't experienced. After trying everything, I can honestly tell you, health goes *way beyond* diet. The word *die*t (key word "die") subconsciously keeps people trapped in a left-brain way of thinking. Whenever you are in a left-brain way of thinking you are on a carnal, physical level and the greater part of you will stay asleep causing you to never be able to see the full truth. The reason why there are a million diets that don't work is because humans are tackling the problem from a completely physical level of thinking.

The main principle of nutrition is that it's not about what you eat, it's about what you don't eat. And to know what not to eat, you must understand the game of food. There are billions of dollars invested into the food industry, and like most industries, it's a money game. Marketers understand human nature and how our brains operate from a level that we don't even know about. It's a game you've been locked into and has been rigged so you can't win. We've been in this game since we were born and most of us don't even know it. But you have an opportunity to escape the game.

When it comes to food, we've become slavishly dependent on something that isn't necessarily important in our lives. Just like a crackhead is addicted to crack, we've become addicted to food. If you stop giving a crackhead crack, he will feel weak because he believes he needs that drug to live. The same occurs when we stop giving the body chemicals and drugs found in processed foods that keep us addicted. We have been programmed and conditioned to live off of these drugs that we call food. When we stop giving ourselves food (drugs), we feel sick and like we are going to die. That's why people get headaches and don't feel well when they stop eating because it's a drug.

Now, I want to be clear. I'm not just telling you to stop eating altogether. That's insanity. But it is key to have an awareness that food is an addiction, and every time I'm eating, I'm feeding an addiction. You aren't feeding yourself nutrients. I don't care what you are eating - Paleo, vegan, etc. - you are just feeding an addiction, and the body slowly becomes a toxic cesspool because it's overwhelmed with toxins from the food you eat.

A lot, if not all the foods that are marketed and promoted are chemicals, drugs, and processed garbage, among other things that are not designed to be in the human body. The impact of consuming these foods has major consequences. By consuming these chemicals, they start to sabotage our taste buds as they enter our bloodstream, and we start to become addicted and chemically dependent on this garbage.

Consuming these non-foods also puts excess strain on your organs, excess waste into your body, and alters your DNA. A huge reason why some individuals cannot achieve the body they desire and work so hard for is because of the consumption of food that was never intended to be in the human body. The formulas of these foods and the formulas of our bodies do not match. The reason our society is growing sicker, fatter, and more depressed each day has a lot to do with processed food consumption.

Lastly, consuming these non-foods lowers our vibrational frequency and numbs us to the true nature of reality. We start to get comfortable, watch mindless TV, fall into the illusion of money and power, and get locked into our ego self rather than our true selves.

Here is a list of some things that have no place in a human body.

- *Sugar* - if the product has the word "sugar" on the label do not eat it. It's a processed chemical.

- *Salt* - if a product has "salt" on the label, do not eat (use sea salt instead)

- *Artificial or Natural Flavors*

- *High Fructose Corn Syrup*

- *Dairy Products* - unless you have access to pure raw milk from grass-fed cows

- *Canned foods*

- *White Flour, white rice, white bread*

- *Shellfish*

- *Pork*

- *Cold Cuts* - (Processed meats)

- *Fruit Juices*

Everything, including food, is information, but we have been programmed to believe food is something to appease our fleshly cravings. Food is meant to receive and give back information, but we have turned it into a fleshly game of indulgence. We've lost the true meaning of what food is designed for. Finding the best sources of information is not always physical. Looking at Nikola Tesla's quote from the beginning of the chapter, if you think of the Universe in terms of energy, frequency and vibration, then you won't get locked into the game of calories, protein, and fats; rather, you will think in terms of energy.

The less physical food you put into your body, the better your body will operate and the more room you will have for your energy to express itself. Think about when you clean out a room in your house. When the room is crowded with furniture and clutter, it can make the room seem smaller and more constrained. However, when you start cleaning the room and clearing out the clutter, you make more space for movement and freedom. The same is true for our bodies. In terms of nutrition, we have been pushed towards mass consumption because the economy wants to make us believe that physical food is what sustains us while people are dying simply because of overeating.

All the physical food inside of you weighs you down and hinders your vibration and frequency, but no one wants you to know that less is more. That would go against every book, every commercial, every propaganda machine, every fast-food chain, etc. It would literally destroy the infrastructure of America. But less really is more. You don't always have to be trapped into the "three meals a day and a snack" philosophy. As you realize less is more, you will be stronger and more athletic. You will be able to vibrate on a higher frequency because you aren't weighed down by the dense food suffocating your spirit.

Similar to cleaning out a room, when you start to clean out your body, your energy will feel much better because there will be more space for Spirit and energy to come in, which you were crowding out with physical stuff. When we are physically cleaned out, we are making more room for Spirit to come in. One of the best ways to overcome your addiction to food is by fasting.

As I said earlier, I'm not suggesting at all that you should stop eating altogether. But starting with intermittent fasting will help you cut back gradually. Intermittent fasting is when you cycle between periods of eating and then not eating. Start with 12 hours, then 16, then 20. It might take you ten years to fast for a whole day, but the point is to stop eating meat, processed food, starches, grains and a number of other foods that are swelling your body. And each time you eat, have an awareness that you are feeding an addiction. The purpose of fasting is to train your body to live off of a different energy source because everything is energy, and everything is light.

To go deeper, matter doesn't exist. That's something we've constructed in our minds. Instead, everything has a frequency and a vibration, which is fed by energy. Therefore, finding the cleanest and best sources of energy should be your focus. Most of the time, it's not physical food sources that we need. The foundation of your nutrition should be the energy you get from sunlight, oxygen and water. Once you realize that, you can start thinking about what you like to eat as a part of your physical structure. Eat things that have the highest frequency, not from a fleshly standpoint but from the highest level of nourishment that feeds your entire body to include mental, emotional, and spiritual.

Your physical body is only a small part of who you are and *all* aspects of you must be fed. While there are many bodies, there are 4 main ones I want to focus on here -- spiritual, mental, emotional, and physical. All these bodies are interconnected so you cannot work on one without simultaneously working on them all.

The *spiritual body* feeds off connecting to the highest version of yourself. You feed this body by doing what you love *every day*. Living a life of purpose and being authentic about who you are as a being is a major food source for the spiritual body.

The *mental body* feeds off knowledge and learning deep universal truths that help to expand your awareness and consciousness. Growth hormones are released every time you expand and grow your consciousness. Consciousness is infinite, and you can always choose to expand and grow your consciousness.

The *emotional body* feeds off of deep meaningful relationships and the right connections.

The *physical body* feeds on proper nutrients such as oxygen, sunlight, water, minerals, etc.

Expanding your view on nutrition that goes far beyond the third dimension into the fifth dimension will show you that feeding really has nothing to do with food and the physical body is just a small portion of the bodies that need to be fed every day. This concept easily takes the focus away from needing to make another trip to the grocery store or stopping at a drive-thru on the way home. Now, you can focus on feeding all your bodies from the sources we've been provided by the Universe since birth.

Chapter 9

Cellular Integrity

It sounds good to believe that food is giving us nutrients to sustain our body. We feel like we are getting nutrients from food, but nothing can sustain what it can't produce. If food and drink can't produce a person, how can it sustain a person? What can produce a person is oxygen, sunlight, water, and energy (our bodies are just masses of energy). We are walking light. Our bodies are made of light, which is the same thing that sustains the sun, moon, stars, and plants. We are literally made of star dust energy, so if they don't need food and drink to sustain, why the fuck do I need it to sustain me?

The illusion that food is what sustains us is why the body breaks down so quickly. If someone wants to argue this point, you will lose 1000 times out of 1000. All these diets keep us chasing our tails. We think it's got to be the food to get a six pack; it's got to be the food to get strong; maybe a new concoction; a new potion; a new diet; extra meat; grass-fed;

no food - it all boils down to people just chasing their fucking tail.

If we are light beings, then what should we eat instead of just food? The answer is, once you start to feed yourself with true life, your body will build back upon the true source that God designed for you - oxygen, sunlight and the real nutrients in the air. If people knew how many nutrients are in the air, they wouldn't even think about going to the grocery store. But the body can't even think because it's so overwhelmed with toxins from the food we eat.

We are formulas walking around here, but our bodies can't accept the proper formulas because we've been feeding it a foreign substance since the day we were born. That's why we are fucked up physically and emotionally because we are living in a world that's not designed for who we are, which are light beings. This world is trying to box us into the third dimension. It's like putting light in chains, but the chains we have are the paradigms we embrace.

The air and the nutrients in the air are the bodybuilders. These are what truly give our cells life and energy to build. The nourishment we need is surrounding us, and breathing practices are actually what feed the cells. Walking on the ground barefoot brings energy (nourishment) into your body from the ground. The sun brings radiation to the body with so many benefits. I actually refer to this type of food source as "SolFood." It is a spin-off of the word "soul food" which describes the deep southern, ethnic (black) style of cooking and eating. Normally if someone says I'm eating soul-food, this means deep fried this, fried that, tons of grease, butter, fats, sugars, and other foods that contribute to a sick, obese, toxic, low vibrational, and foul way of living.

The funny thing is a lot of people take pride in that form of filthy consumption. They almost wear it as a badge of honor. I feel it is my responsibility to change the narrative from the old slave mentality. The reason why most ethnic groups take pride in that term is because it connects them as a group. Soul food was the only food they were allowed to eat as slaves, so they made the most of it. I get it, honestly. I was raised on some good ol' soul food.

Now that I'm in my 40s and have learned the error of my ways, I choose not to play the game set before me. I'm playing my own game. This next generation will know and learn about a new Solfood. One that is truly good for the soul. The new Solfood is a source of true nourishment, positive emotions, energy, mood enhancement, and the balancing of the mind and hormones. It is the most powerful energy source in the world (the light of the world).

There are even more benefits of consuming the necessary amount of Solfood each day:

1. Vitamin D (which is actually a hormone)

2. Improved Mood and Sense of Well Being

3. Instant Energy Boost

4. Increases Lifespan

5. Creates Serotonin (feel good chemical)

6. Strengthens Bones

7. Burns Fat

8. Prevents Cancer

9. Heals Skin Conditions

10. Regulates Blood Pressure

11. Enhances Creativity

12. Better Sleep

13. Helps Body Produce its own Protein, Muscle Tone and Elasticity

14. Balance Hormones

The list of benefits of daily Solfood is endless. I recommend everyone to be getting at least 30 minutes of direct sunlight daily. If you have a darker complexion, the minimum should be 60 minutes. Solfood along with other natural nutrient sources we've covered are more subtle forms of energy that can set you free as a spiritual being and take the chains off of you. It will raise your level of awareness because it will let you realize that your mind is the mover. As you raise your level of awareness through minimizing substances that merely weigh you down (both physically and spiritually) you have more control of your reality.

With each new level of awareness, you will have more power in this third dimension.

As you keep bogging yourself down with food and chemicals and think you need to feed this fleshly body, you bring yourself down to a low frequency and vibration. Frequency and vibration are your attraction points. Once you understand that you are attracting at all times, you start to change your attraction point. As you raise your level of awareness, you will attract differently. When you're feeding your body with food as an addiction, your cells will start to swell, lowering your vibration and frequency. Humans are designed to have 360 senses, yet we are down to five, and as you continue to burden your physical organs with dense food, you are shutting down your psychic abilities, imagination power, access to the infinite realm where creation takes place, clairvoyance, etc. We are supposed to be fucking gods walking the Earth. I should be able to travel to Dubai to see what the fuck is going on there, but food is dulling us down to third dimensional nothingness.

Strengthening cellular integrity happens from the inside out. Most people build their cells from the outside, but they become weak and decrepit and must take testosterone or estrogen because they haven't done the work from the inside out. To improve cellular integrity, you can start implementing these daily practices to feed your cells properly.

1. Mini Trampoline - When you jump on a mini trampoline, you suspend yourself in the air, which strengthens and

protects your cells. Doing light jumps on the mini rebound personally separates you and shows you the resiliency and control of your body from a cellular level, out as opposed to a muscular level, in.

2. Eat light and eat light - When I'm not eating or weighing my body down with food, my cells can vibrate faster. If I'm eating, then it slows down my vibration because my cells start swelling up. This is where fasting can be used to tap into a higher energy source because without food or with a smaller amount of food, your body vibrates higher. High vibration helps you think more clearly, be more creative, elevates your thoughts, and keeps you from becoming so emotional. Fasting, whether it is intermittent or full day fasts, tunes you into a different frequency. If people really understood that vibration, frequency and energy are real and we aren't our body, they would think twice about what they put inside their body.

Eating light then allows you to eat light, which are the elements we went over earlier in the chapter. Removing your addiction from the food that we are sold to boost the economy and keep us sick will allow us to eat light so that we can really eat light. Remember, cells are the bodybuilders. We believe food builds the body, and that is so fucking false. Air and oxygen are what the cells thrive on, and cells are what build the body. The food we are sold is really not a needed human resource; rather, it's needed to keep the economy moving.

Section 4

Environment

Chapter 10

Who Do you Listen to?

I t's impossible to start this section without resurfacing a quote I used earlier on in the book. Never, and a million times ever, listen to anyone in any field who is not experiencing the results that you are wanting to produce. Let me say it again. Never. It's such a simple statement, but for some reason, we are listening to people who have the right charisma, the right words, the right clothes, and the right material possessions, but their lives are showing that they don't really know what they are talking about. It's all smoke and mirrors. Because if people really knew the truth they were trying to tell you, then they would be experiencing it. The truth is, their *opinions* may seem right, but their life shows that it's wrong.

You wouldn't go to a homeless guy and ask him for financial advice. You wouldn't go to a trainer that is overweight and ask them how to get healthy. You wouldn't go to a lawyer who is losing all of his cases and ask him to represent you in court. So, why are we going to all these "experts" and accepting their opinions at face value?

If you want to be a high jumper, find someone who is jumping high. Don't go to someone who used to jump high or someone who has read about how to jump high or someone who has done research on jumping high without actually experiencing it themselves. I wouldn't listen to someone who is rich with a silver spoon in his mouth, a stable of horses, and a 100 million dollars in his back account. Why? Because he hasn't been where I've been. He didn't have to go through what I went through. So, his path won't be the same as my path. That's why you should only listen to a motherfucker that has been where you've been and is currently experiencing what you want to experience. I want to talk to a motherfucker that grew up a latchkey kid with a single mother, getting the lights turned out. I want to hear how he got to the top while going through those struggles because that person is going to be able to help me.

There is so much misinformation, propaganda, and lies out there, and you may be going backwards for years by listening to one wrong person or applying one wrong piece of information. It can fuck up your entire life. People are spewing so much misinformation that they've heard from someone else, and it's become like a game of telephone. The point of the game is that each person is supposed to repeat the statement whispered in their ear, but as the information travels down the line from person to person, the original message becomes distorted.

Everyone is essentially creating an illusion with the opinions they share, but they view their opinions as fact. Even the Bible says that every man is right in his own mind. But everything is just an illusion. And if that illusion is not what you want to produce, you must tune them out fast. There are a lot of great talkers out here but not many people actually doing what they are talking about. That's where the illusion comes into play. To know and not to do is really not to know, so motherfucker, if you can't show me, then shut the fuck up.

The first and foremost person you need to listen to is yourself. You must have a clear conscience if you want to get to that point so you can lean into your intuition. To do this, you have to unplug and tap back into alignment with yourself. Once you tap back in, then you will be more discerning and be able to walk around with a new set of glasses. Tapping back into yourself is unplugging from any person, place, idea, possession, etc. that's not serving you or pushing you forward. Get rid of your distractions. Minimize and remove everything from your life that's not in alignment with where you want to be.

This part is hard because we have been taught to look for external validation from external resources. If we have a question, we go straight to Google instead of asking ourselves. We go to "experts" or "influencers" or "leaders" for advice and affirmation. However, our infinite selves already know everything. Dig inside and investigate what and who you are embracing. To clear your conscience and get the answers you are seeking, you must cut down on the noise that is in your head and give space to listen to what you are trying to tell you. Who you truly are is trying to talk to you. Your highest-level self gives you codes, symbols and puts people in your way to get your attention. Being quiet allows you to tune in to what the right information for you is. You can go into your head right now and ask any fucking question imaginable, and you will get an answer. And rest assured, that answer is what really you needed to hear.

You also must know what the fuck you want. If you don't know what you want, you are like a ship without a rudder and miserable as fuck because you are going in circles. When you unplug to tune back into yourself and discover what you really want, then the people you need will start to show up because you will be more congruent with where you are going. You will also be more discerning of the people who come into your life. If someone doesn't fit, you will be able to tune them out.

When you are determining who to listen to, don't just look at what you can see. Don't judge the book just by its cover. Answer these questions: Is this person experiencing what I want to produce? Is this person knowledgeable and personally acting upon that knowledge? Is this person's words and lifestyle aligning with what my highest self is already speaking to me about? Are this person's history and life struggles similar to mine? Getting these answers first will minimize your propensity to blindly accept people and information without testing what you embrace.

Chapter 11

Take 100 % Responsibility

Imagine that you are sitting in a room, and someone walks up to you and slaps you in the face. Sit in that for a minute because I'm about to follow it up with a hard truth that is going to take the rest of your life to learn and accept. *That* was *your* responsibility. Why? Because whether you like it or not, everything in your reality was created by you. You created your parents, your kids, where you lived, your body, your sickness - everything in your reality was created by you. I call this concept the 5-second miracle.

The 5-second miracle is taking 100% responsibility for everything that happens in your life. Why do I call this a miracle? This is a miracle because it automatically takes you from victim to creator, which is the most impactful paradigm shift that will ever happen in your life. This is when you take full and absolute control over your reality and no longer have the disease of mysticism that would have you to believe that you are a passive participant with little to no control over your life.

Taking 100% responsibility was one of the toughest pills for me to swallow, but every day I take this pill. If someone cuts me off in traffic (I created it); someone cheats on me in a relationship (I created it); I get sick (I created it); I'm injured and fat (I created it); I hit the lottery (I created it); I meet the perfect person (I created it). No matter what happens or shows up on the screen of my life, I created it. Some will read this and not want to accept this and that's fine. You will just belong to the 95% that play victim and always have an excuse for themselves.

The ones that choose to experience this miracle and have this mindset embedded will begin to trace all effects back to their causes. This is where all the magic (deep inner work) takes place. We can then go on the journey of making the unconscious conscious and become aware of how we are creating our reality at all times (health, wealth, relationships, fitness, business, etc). At this point we become aware of the power of our beliefs, our words, the people we choose to surround ourselves with, the foods we consume, the music and things we listen to, the books we read, our habits and more.

After this miracle, you will no longer belong to the people that are living at effect. You will be part of the few who take 100% responsibility for their body, health, fitness, etc. You will understand from this day forward you can have, be, and do whatever you want because you are the creator and never the victim.

You are the great creator, and if all is mind and everything in the Universe is mental, then your mind is always creating. When you accept your role as the creator you begin to see things from different levels because people who play victim are never going to be introspective nor will they grow. You can't grow being a victim because it will be too easy to blame your parents, spouse, partner, the government, conspiracy theorists, the weather, society, the environment you grew up in, the fast-food industry, or any other outside source. Playing the victim is a comfortable and ego driven place to be in. However, it's also a dead state because you can no longer grow in this place. It's actually the weakest position to be in. When you are a victim, you hand all of your power away.

Do you want the 5-second miracle operating in your life? You have to take 100% responsibility for *everything* that has happened in your life. This is the most important foundational piece of your health. It's tough to create from a weak body. The stronger your physical, spiritual, emotional and mental bodies are, the better your faculties operate. Your ability to create will be like magic.

Many of us have experienced difficult situations or dealt with trauma, and it can be tough to hear that you must take 100% responsibility. You don't have to have a full understanding of what happened to you. But if you take 100% responsibility for creating it and accept it as a learning experience, then there is an opportunity for you to grow. There is no such thing as good and bad, it just is. Everything in your life comes to you so you can grow. The person that was rejected, the person that was stabbed, and the person that was abused are the types of people that the Universe loves the most. As fucked up as that sounds, the lower you go, the higher you go up. That's science -- the harder you bounce the ball, the higher it goes back up.

The universal concept of vibration and frequency will help you understand why situations occurred in your life. You will then understand why you got in that car accident, why you got rejected, why your spouse hit you, why you got fired from your job, etc. As you think, you create. And as you feel, you attract since everything is vibration. Let's say I'm a negative mood. I'm mad and pissed off, and then I leave and get into a car accident that causes me to be even more mad, pissed off and angry. What happened there was the Universe just answered my wish because I was looking for more to fuel my anger. Later on, I might find out that my girlfriend was cheating on me because the Universe sees that I'm looking for more situations that will fuel my anger. That's how this works. I'm the fucking creator. Whatever I wish, I'm a genie. My mind is the lamp. I can create anything I want just by feeling and the Universe will grant every wish based on those feelings.

The world is your kaleidoscope and things are always moving. You are going to go through so many different types of scenarios in your life, but the most important decision you can ever make in your life is prioritizing these two pillars in your life - your health and self-love. This will help with taking 100% responsibility and shifting your paradigm with the energy you are giving and receiving. Fuck getting a car, a house, a relationship - all those things paint the coat on your house, but what really matters is what's inside. As you love yourself, the love you give yourself will return at the exact proportion to how much you love you give. And as healthy as you become, your reality will mirror that health back to you.

Chapter 12

As Above and So Below

The hermetic principle "as above so below" speaks to the interconnectedness of everything in our lives. We went over the different bodies in earlier chapters, but there are so many more different bodies that have to be tended to and taken care of. Just viewing yourself as a physical being will keep you in bondage. As we discussed earlier, we are so much more than that. But if you start taking care of your physical body, the rest will be taken care of unbeknownst to you. You must start with awareness of these multiple bodies that need to be cared for. The physical body has to be in alignment with your mental, your spiritual, your angelic, your astro, and other bodies. Once you take responsibility for your life, you will use this law of correspondence to clean out parts of your life that need to be corrected - from smallest to largest.

"As above, so below" means you can understand the larger system by understanding the smaller system and vice versa.

Everything you put inside of you has an equal or opposite expression on the outside. The as above so below principle gives you power to place on the inside what you want on the outside. If you want a chaotic home, then put chaos inside. If you want a dirty exterior environment, keep the interior dirty. Whatever you are seeing manifest on the outside of you is connected to something that is residing on the inside of you. Your physical reality is just a mirrored expression of the spiritual reality inside of you.

This principle is not one that has to be incredibly complex. It is merely an awareness and then a decision to be made. The awareness is really taking the time to observe your physical reality. What is happening around you? After you assess your current physical reality, then it's time to get to work. This is where we mess up. We think the work is in focusing on our physical reality. We want to change others or manipulate and control situations to work out in our favor. This is wasted time and effort. The real work that has proven results is to focus on the inside.

There are daily practices that you can implement that will help you see more clearly. Sometimes the work is just in removing and getting out of our own way.

1. Fasting – as you fast you raise your frequency and self-awareness.

2. Cleanliness/Organization – look at your home, office, car – how can you implement cleanliness and organization

into those environments that will then bring cleanliness and organization to the inside.

3. Go to the ant to look at their ways and be wise - ants put first things first to optimize their time, resources, and skills. They utilize teamwork and strategic planning to get the job done.

4. Meditation – start with 5 minutes a day.

5. Remove clutter – this can be physical clutter around you or clutter from your mind.

Chapter 13

Nonattachment

Another bitter pill to swallow is nonattachment. In the third dimensional realm, attachment to people and things can happen when you forget that everything merely exists in your mind. That is the definition of insanity. When you attach yourself to things and people as if they are a part of you, you are an insane person. You can't just get attached to a mind trip. Because when you attach yourself to something, you get pulled down to a lower vibrational state. As we attach, we feel like we *need* something, which means if you get it, it adds, but if you lose it, it subtracts.

Nothing is external from you. You can visualize that something is there in that moment, but it's not, which means if it leaves it will take nothing away from you. You will still be the same being tomorrow as you were today. This digs deep when it comes to relationships and material possessions because you own nothing. You can enjoy things, but they do not define you nor do they create who you are as a being. It is just an experience.

I have to remind myself of this shit all the time because it's so easy to get plugged into this third dimension, which makes you feel like things will make you better.

You feel a sense of belonging when you attach yourself to a certain group, sector, title, partner - and once you lose it, it feels like you are losing a part of you. If I'm a doctor or an attorney and I get fired from my job that I was attached to, I would feel like a part of me died. This happened when the stock market crashed. There were people jumping out of buildings in New York City because they were so attached to physical money. If you are in a relationship with someone and that person leaves you or cheats on you, your ego driven, third dimensional self will feel like you lost a part of yourself.

You shouldn't be attached to people, places, things, labels, anything. You've got to understand that this shit is a game, and everything is just an agreement that we are all abiding by. We agree that $100 is $100, but it is just a piece of paper. It is merely an agreement. But we are so stuck in our ego and have been trained to be third dimensional slaves to feel like this is real. So, if we don't have the car, the house, the boat, the partner, or whatever else society tells us we should have, we feel like we are less than if we don't have it. And then when we get it, we want more because we are attached to these illusions. But once you understand they are illusions, you can detach from these expectations, opinions, and false belief systems.

In my opinion, the worst thing that ever happened to the world is religion because it taught people to attach to something external. It created a false belief that we need something outside of ourselves. Once you get in the habit of attaching to something external from you, you are on the fast track to depression and misery. Nonattachment is having the awareness that you don't own anything, which means nothing owns you. It can be easier to digest this when it comes to physical things, but it seems like when it comes to people, we can struggle more with this. Even your kids -- you don't own them. Any of your relationships -- you don't own that person. First, they exist in your mind and have their own universe. They are a universe unto themselves, so you have to let them be what and who they are. Many times in relationships, people try to control their partner and dictate how they act and operate instead of letting them express their existence however they want to. We claim ownership of other people because we've been trained to feel like these are "my kids," "my wife," "my husband," "my friend." Words are powerful, so once you put "my" on something, you create attachment.

These beings are spirits. You can't own a spiritual being having a spiritual experience. Even with this truth, relationships can still be difficult to remain detached from because there are so many feelings and emotions involved. That's why people go through depression after a break-up because they feel like they lost a part of themselves. They feel dead inside. But it's all just our ego and insecurities in full operation.

I'm not saying that you shouldn't have human emotions and feelings and you just need to be cold hearted. All I'm saying is to allow those feelings to come without hanging on and being attached. If I get out of a relationship, I can still be hurt without hanging on. Because if I did, I would be sick and depressed. I would be attached to something that is simply part of my human experience. People's energy is flowing in and out of your life. You can feel the emotions of that flow but have the awareness that it's just an experience. Have your emotions, but don't let them take over your life.

The paradigm shift of nonattachment is centered around awareness. It takes a certain level of awareness to understand that you are creating everything in your head. You have to understand that you are drawing in everything from your energy and your thoughts. The Universe is a big ass thought, and everything is energy. And the people you are hanging out with are vibrational beings. They exist in more than just a third dimensional being. Having that awareness allows you to understand that your only responsibility is to be the highest version of you. You should want everything else to express itself the way they want to and the way they need to without you having to control them. If your girlfriend cheated on you, then she wanted to cheat on you. If your boyfriend didn't call you, then he didn't want to call you. You can't control that. We are so ego inflated that we don't just release that. Your only job is to be the highest version of you. And people that are attracted to that version of you are the people that are supposed to be in your life. If someone decides that they are going to do something that doesn't agree with you, then you get them out of your life.

Chapter 14

The Infinity Way

I just want to take this final chapter and thank you for being a part of this book and journey. It is my hope that you have reached a higher level of frequency and vibration that will allow these concepts to become a part of your reality. Personally, I feel like I live in a world that most people don't even know exists yet. Some people will take lifetimes before these concepts enter their reality. So, for you to have these concepts to reach this point makes me feel honored and blessed to be the one to bring them to you to further your journey.

With that being said, realize that the flesh profits nothing, but it is the spirit that is quickened. We were born and live in a machine. Realize that almost all of your thoughts have been programmed by this machine and unplugging isn't going to be easy. There will be ebbs and flows and ups and downs. But at the same time, through all seeming chaos, there is order. It's chaos then order, chaos then order. Know that when you are going through chaos that you are leveling up. Comfort is a drug, and if you are comfortable, you aren't growing.

There will be times when you will feel really good. You will feel on top of the world and like your spirit is working for you and you are working for your spirit. You will be locked into a higher dimension as your thoughts are elevated. And then you will feel like your world is being flipped upside down. But the chaos is for your growth and development. Everything is love, and love is what prompts your growth. It's all about growth, and growth is a process.

We were trained to see life from a linear perspective. In this world, we go from first grade to second grade to college to grad school and so on. But life really isn't a linear experience. It is a cyclical life that is always returning you back to where you started. But when you return to the start, you come with more awareness and a better opportunity to experience life differently. Realize that all of this is a journey, and it's not an overnight process. It's worth it in the long run.

May this book be a consistent source of encouragement and motivation as you embark on your fitness journey. And as we discussed in the book, this journey goes way beyond what we have ever been taught or imagined. We have our many bodies, but we haven't been taught how to feed these bodies. As I learn and grow in my development, I will continue to share my thoughts and opinions with you. Let's continue to grow and get better together. Most importantly, let's disrupt this fitness game as we elevate to higher levels of consciousness. Peace!

Printed in Great Britain
by Amazon

79914159R00066